The Legend of King Arthur and His Knights of the Round Table

COLORING BOOK

The legend of King Arthur and his knights of the Round Table began in Great Britain during medieval times. In the story, young Arthur draws a sword from an enchanted stone, a sign that he is to be the next king of England. Arthur becomes a great and noble king and holds court at Camelot, where he and his valiant knights gather at the Round Table for meetings and feasts. Knights of the Round Table must uphold the highest standards of conduct and be truthful, brave, and kind. They often face great danger to rescue people who need their help.

The legend involves many people—including King Arthur and Queen Guinevere, the wizard Merlin, knights of the Round Table such as Sir Lancelot and Sir Galahad, and more—and many interesting places, dragons and other animals, and enchanted objects such as the sword Excalibur, given to King Arthur by the mysterious Lady of the Lake.

In this coloring book you'll find 22 line drawings illustrating parts of the Arthurian legend. These drawings were inspired by paintings made by three famous artists about a century ago—the paintings are shown as small colored pictures on the inside front and back covers of this book. When you color in the drawings, you might enjoy using the colors in the original paintings, or you might have fun choosing your own.

We left the last page of this book blank so that you can draw and color a picture of your own. Will it be a knight on horseback, a dragon, Merlin, or another part of the legend of King Arthur?

Pomegranate **kids**®

1. Walter Crane,* *Young Owen Appeals to the King*
2. Walter Crane, *Arthur Draws the Sword from the Stone*
3. Arthur Rackham,† *How Galahad Drew Out the Sword from the Floating Stone at Camelot*
4. Walter Crane, *King Arthur Asks the Lady of the Lake for the Sword Excalibur*
5. Arthur Rackham, *How Sir Launcelot Fought with a Fiendly Dragon*
6. Walter Crane, *Beaumains Wins the Fight at the Ford*
7. Walter Crane, *The Witch Gives Advice as to Sir Tristram's Wound*
8. Eleanor Fortescue Brickdale,‡ *Elaine and Lancelot*
9. Walter Crane, *Sir Geraint and the Lady Enid in the Deserted Roman Town*
10. Eleanor Fortescue Brickdale, *Geraint in Rusty Armor*
11. Walter Crane, *Young Perceval Questions Sir Owen*
12. Arthur Rackham, *How Queen Guenever Rode a-Maying into the Woods and Fields Beside Westminster*
13. Walter Crane, *Perceval Obtains the Shield of the Beating Heart*
14. Eleanor Fortescue Brickdale, *Enid*
15. Walter Crane, *Sir Owen Greets the Lady of the Fountain*
16. Arthur Rackham, *Merlin and Nimue: How by Her Subtle Working She Made Merlin to Go Under the Stone to Let Her Wit of the Marvels There: And She Wrought So There for Him That He Came Never Out for All the Craft He Could Do*
17. Eleanor Fortescue Brickdale, *Elaine with Lancelot's Shield*
18. Walter Crane, *Sir Galahad Is Brought to the Court of King Arthur*
19. Arthur Rackham, *How at a Great Feast That King Mark Made Came Eliot the Harper and Sang the Lay That Dinadan Had Made*
20. Walter Crane, *The Fight in the Queen's Ante-chamber*
21. Walter Crane, *Sir Lancelot Forbids Sir Bors to Slay the King*
22. Walter Crane, *Sir Bedevere Casts the Sword Excalibur into the Lake*

*Illustrations by Walter Crane (English, 1845–1915) are from *King Arthur's Knights: The Tales Re-told for Boys and Girls*, by Henry Gilbert (Edinburgh: T. C. and E. C. Jack, 1911).

†Illustrations by Arthur Rackham (English, 1867–1939) are from *The Romance of King Arthur and His Knights of the Round Table: Abridged from Malory's Morte d'Arthur*, by Alfred W. Pollard (New York: Macmillan, 1917).

‡Illustrations by Eleanor Fortescue Brickdale (English, 1872–1945) are from *Idylls of the King*, by Alfred, Lord Tennyson (London: Hodder and Stoughton, 1911).

Pomegranate Communications, Inc.
Box 808022, Petaluma CA 94975
800 227 1428   www.pomegranate.com

© 2010 Pomegranate Communications, Inc.

Catalog No. CB124

Designed and rendered by Oky Sulistio

Printed in Korea

19 18 17 16 15 14 13 12 11 10   10 9 8 7 6 5 4 3 2 1

Pomegranate Europe Ltd.
Unit 1, Heathcote Business Centre, Hurlbutt Road
Warwick, Warwickshire CV34 6TD, UK
[+44] 0 1926 430111
sales@pomeurope.co.uk

This product is in compliance with the Consumer Product Safety Improvement Act of 2008 (CPSIA).
A General Conformity Certificate concerning Pomegranate's compliance with the CPSIA is available on our website at www.pomegranate.com, or by request at 800 227 1428.
For additional CPSIA-required tracking details, contact Pomegranate at 800 227 1428.

1. Young Owen appeals to King Arthur for help.

2. Young Arthur draws a sword from an enchanted stone.

Thomas

3. Sir ~~Galahad~~ removes a sword from a floating stone at Camelot.

4. King Arthur asks the Lady of the Lake for the sword Excalibur.

5. Sir Lancelot fights with a fiery dragon.

6. Sir Gareth (Sir Beaumains) battles foes at a ford in a river.

7. An old woman tells King Mark how to heal Sir Tristan's wound.

8. Elaine of Astolat speaks with Sir Lancelot.

King Archer
9. Sir Geraint and Lady Enid ride through a deserted town.

10. Sir Geraint rides to a tournament in rusty borrowed armor.

11. Young Perceval questions Sir Owen.

12. Queen Guinevere takes a springtime ride through the countryside.

13. Sir Perceval obtains the Shield of the Beating Heart.

14. Lady Enid prepares to welcome a guest.

15. Sir Owen greets the Lady of the Fountain.

16. Nimue tricks Merlin into entering a cave.

17. Elaine of Astolat carries Sir Lancelot's shield.

18. Sir Galahad is brought to the court of King Arthur.

19. A minstrel sings a song that Sir Dinadan wrote to insult King Mark.

20. A fight erupts outside Queen Guinevere's chambers.

21. Sir Lancelot prevents Sir Bors from slaying King Arthur.

22. Sir Bedivere casts the sword Excalibur back into the lake.

Draw and color your own picture here!